TOSEL®

READING SERIES

PRE-STARTER

READING

3

 International TOSEL Committee

CONTENTS

About TOSEL®

TOSEL (Test of Skills in the English Language) was developed to meet the demand for a more effective assessment of English as a foreign language for learners from specific cultural settings.

TOSEL evaluates and certifies the proficiency levels of English learners, from the age of 4 through adulthood, along with academic and job performance results.

Background

- Other English tests are ineffective in accurately measuring individual abilities
- Overuse of US-dominated testing systems in diverse cultural and educational contexts in the global English language learning market

Functions & Usage

- Assessment is categorized into 7 levels
- Used as a qualification for academic excellence for school admissions
- Used as a test to assess the English proficiency in the corporate and public sectors

Goals

- Create an effective tool for assessing and evaluating the English skills of English language learners
- Implement efficient and accessible testing systems and methods
- Provide constructive and developmental English education guidance

TOSEL® Strength

LEVELED ASSESSMENTS

An established English test system fit for seven different levels according to learners' cognitive development

ACCURATE DIAGNOSIS

A systematic and scientific diagnosis of learners' English proficiency

EXTENSIVE MATERIALS

Supplementary materials to help learners in an EFL environment to prepare for TOSEL and improve their proficiency

SUFFICIENT DATA

Content for each level developed by using data accumulated from more than 2,000,000 TOSEL test takers delegated at 15,000 schools and academies

CLASSIFIED AREAS OF INTELLIGENCE

Content designed to foster and expand the strengths of each student, categorized by the eight areas of intelligence

CONTINUITY

A complete course of English education ranging from kindergarten, elementary school, middle school, high schoool, and up to adults.

HIGH RELIABILITY

A high reliability level (Cronbach's alpha: .904 for elementary school students / .864 for university students) proven by several studies (Oxford University / Modern Language Journal)

SYSTEMATIC & EFFECTIVE ENGLISH EDUCATION

Accurate diagnosis and extensive materials which provide a step-by-step development in English learning, according to the quality of each learner's ability

TOSEL® Level Chart

Seven Separate Assessments

TOSEL divides the test into seven stages, by considering the test takers' cognitive levels, according to different ages. Unlike other assessments based on only one level, TOSEL includes separate assessments for preschool, elementary school, middle school, high school students, and for adults, which also includes both professionals and college students.

TOSEL's reporting system highlights the strengths and weaknesses of each test taker and suggests areas for further development.

COCOON

Suitable for children aged 4-6 (pre-schoolers)

The first step in the TOSEL system, the test is composed of colorful designs and interesting questions to interest young learners and to put them at ease.

Pre-STARTER

Suitable for children aged 7-8 (1st-2nd grades of elementary school)

Evaluates the ability to comprehend simple vocabulary, conversations, and sentences.

STARTER

Suitable for children aged 9-10 (3rd-4th grades of elementary school)

Evaluates the ability to comprehend short sentences and conversations related to everyday situations or topics.

BASIC

Suitable for children aged 11-12 (5th–6th grades of elementary school)

Evaluates the ability to communicate about personal information, daily activities, future plans, and past experiences in written and spoken language.

JUNIOR

Suitable for middle school students

Evaluates the ability to comprehend short paragraphs, practical texts, and speech covering general topics and to participate in simple daily conversations.

HIGH JUNIOR

Suitable for high school students

Evaluates the ability to use English fluently, accurately, and effectively on a wide range of social and academic subjects, as well as the ability to use sentences with a variety of complex structures.

ADVANCED

Suitable for university students and adults

Evaluates the ability to use practical English required for a job or work environment, as well as the ability to use and understand English at the university level.

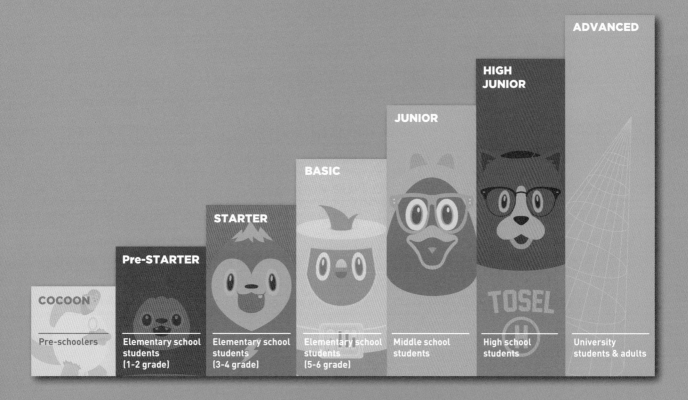

Evaluation

Assessing the Four Skills

TOSEL evaluates the four language skills: reading, listening, speaking and writing, through indirect and direct assessment items.

This system of evaluation is part of a concerted effort to break away from materials geared solely toward grammar and reading-oriented education.

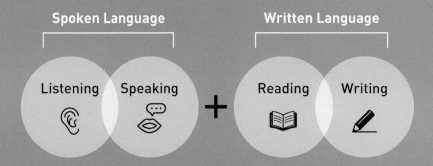

TOSEL Test Information

Level	Score	Grade	Section	
			Section I Listening & Speaking	Section II Reading & Writing
COCOON	100		15 Questions / 15 min	15 Questions / 15 min
Pre-STARTER	100		15 Questions / 15 min	20 Questions / 25 min
STARTER	100		20 Questions / 15 min	20 Questions / 25 min
BASIC	100	1-10	30 Questions / 20 min	30 Questions / 30 min
JUNIOR	100		30 Questions / 20 min	30 Questions / 30 min
HIGH JUNIOR	100		30 Questions / 25 min	35 Questions / 35 min
ADVANCED	990		70 Questions / 45 min	70 Questions / 55 min

Certificates

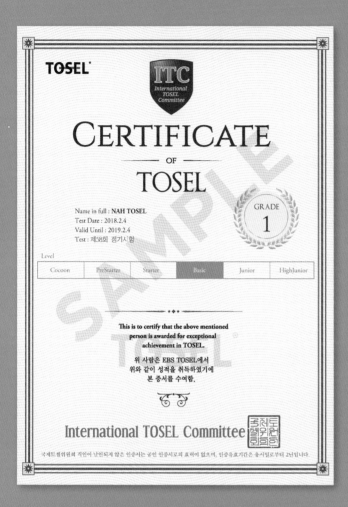

TOSEL Certificate

The International TOSEL Committee officially evaluates and certifies the level of English proficiency of English learners from the age of 4 to adults.

Certified by

Mar. 2010	Korea University
Dec. 2009	The Korean Society of Speech Science
Dec. 2009	The Korea Association of Foreign Language Education
Nov. 2009	The Applied Linguistics Association of Korea
Oct. 2009	The Pan Korea English Teachers Association

CHAPTER 1

People

UNIT 1

Who Is She?

Teacher's Book
p.134

What is your dream job?

This woman wears special clothes. She catches bad people. Sometimes people do bad things. Sometimes people hit others. Sometimes people steal things. Sometimes people drive cars too fast. This woman drives a car. Her car has a loud sound. She drives at night. She protects the town.

New Words

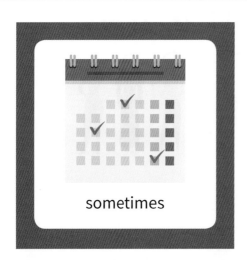

sometimes

steal

drive

loud

Part A. Spell the Words

1.

_stronaut

(A)   a

(B)   e

(C)   o

2.

s_eal

(A)   t

(B)   k

(C)   r

Part B. Situational Writing

3.

Do not _____ other people.

(A)   hit

(B)   help

(C)   protect

4.

The car makes a _____ noise.

(A)   loud

(B)   quiet

(C)   good

5. Who are they?

   (A) cooks

   (B) doctors

   (C) firefighters

6. What are they doing?

   (A) making a fire

   (B) putting out the fire

   (C) playing in the water

Part D. General Reading and Retelling

> This woman wears special clothes. She catches bad people. Sometimes people do bad things. Sometimes people hit others. Sometimes people steal things. Sometimes people drive cars too fast. This woman drives a car. Her car has a loud sound. She drives at night. She protects the town.

7. What is the passage about?

   (A) a job
   (B) a noise
   (C) a bad person

8. Who is she?

   (A) a scientist
   (B) an astronaut
   (C) a police officer

9. What bad things do people do?

   (A) hit others
   (B) save people
   (C) wear special clothes

10. What is NOT true about the woman?

   (A) She drives fast.
   (B) She helps the town.
   (C) She has a noisy car.

Listening Practice

 Listen and write.

  MP3 PS3-1

Who Is She?

This woman wears special clothes. She catches bad people.
[1]_____ people do bad things. Sometimes people hit
others. Sometimes people [2]_____ things. Sometimes
people [3]_____ cars too fast. This woman drives a car.
Her car has a [4]_____ sound. She drives at night. She
protects the town.

Word Bank

lawd	dlive
Somtims	drive
loud	steal
Sometimes	steer

 Listen. Pause. Say each sentence.

  MP3 PS3-1G

Writing Practice

 Write the words.

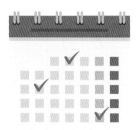

1
s						s

2
s			

3
d			

4
		d	

 Write the words.

Summary

There is a _____. She drives at night. She helps people.

Word Puzzle

C	F	N	C	S	S	A	V	X	C	T	U	V	Q	H
H	L	D	E	N	O	N	D	S	V	R	Q	M	Z	J
K	P	V	F	M	M	V	S	R	E	S	U	N	D	P
X	I	K	Q	X	E	N	H	J	E	T	I	F	H	G
Y	D	S	R	I	T	J	B	F	S	E	O	Q	Z	N
U	J	D	G	U	I	I	R	H	P	A	O	A	N	X
Z	A	L	I	B	M	D	L	U	M	L	E	T	F	K
D	M	O	H	U	E	D	T	L	E	R	A	J	T	R
S	F	S	T	M	S	B	Q	U	K	R	B	J	L	Y
L	D	E	A	R	L	H	A	Z	O	U	W	D	T	B
B	R	C	V	P	W	Y	L	L	O	U	D	P	J	I
P	Z	K	F	D	H	E	Y	K	O	G	B	B	B	K
W	B	V	R	Y	U	Q	V	E	D	D	R	I	V	E
K	E	E	E	M	R	C	F	J	I	V	B	F	V	R
T	B	K	N	R	B	Q	S	Z	Y	C	K	R	Y	P

 Write the words. Then find them in the puzzle.

1 _____ 2 _____ 3 _____ 4 _____

UNIT 2

Zoe Likes Korea

What country do you want to visit?

Zoe lives in Korea. Zoe's father is from Canada. He is Canadian. Zoe's mother is from Mexico. She is Mexican. But now Zoe's family lives in Korea. Zoe goes to a Korean school. Zoe speaks Korean really well. Zoe loves Korean islands. She wants to go to Jeju Island. Zoe's friend is Mina. Mina likes Mexico. But Zoe likes Korea the best.

New Words

Canada

Mexico

Korea

island

Part A. Spell the Words

1.

i_land

(A)   s

(B)   l

(C)   r

2.

K_rea

(A)   o

(B)   i

(C)   a

Part B. Situational Writing

3.

Zoe's father is _____.

(A)   Canada

(B)   Mexican

(C)   Canadian

4.

Zoe's friend likes _____.

(A)   Korea

(B)   Mexico

(C)   Canada

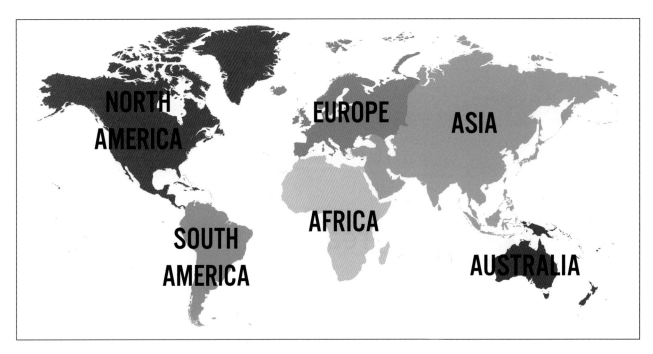

5. What is this?

    (A) World sea
    (B) World map
    (C) World globe

6. What color is Asia?

    (A) red
    (B) green
    (C) yellow

Part D. General Reading and Retelling

> Zoe lives in Korea. Zoe's father is from Canada. He is Canadian. Zoe's mother is from Mexico. She is Mexican. But now Zoe's family lives in Korea. Zoe goes to a Korean school. Zoe speaks Korean really well. Zoe loves Korean islands. She wants to go to Jeju Island. Zoe's friend is Mina. Mina likes Mexico. But Zoe likes Korea the best.

7. What is the best title?

   (A) Zoe Likes Korea
   (B) Zoe Goes to Jeju
   (C) Zoe's Friend Mina

8. Where does Zoe's mother live now?

   (A) in Korea
   (B) in Mexico
   (C) in Canada

9. What is true about Zoe?

   (A) She is learning Spanish.
   (B) She lives in Canada now.
   (C) She goes to a Korean school.

10. Where does Zoe want to go?

   (A) to an island
   (B) to Mina's house
   (C) to a Spanish school

Listening Practice

MP3 PS3-2

Listen and write.

Zoe Likes Korea

Zoe lives in Korea. Zoe's father is from ¹_____. He is Canadian. Zoe's mother is from ²_____. She is Mexican. But now Zoe's family lives in ³_____. Zoe goes to a Korean school. Zoe speaks Korean really well. Zoe loves Korean ⁴_____. She wants to go to Jeju Island. Zoe's friend is Mina. Mina likes Mexico. But Zoe likes Korea the best.

Word Bank

islands	Canada
eye lands	Mekico
Mexico	Korea
korea	Kanada

Listen. Pause. Say each sentence.

MP3 PS3-2G

Writing Practice

 Write the words.

1

| | | | | a |

2

| M | | | | |

3

| | o | | | |

4

| i | | | | |

 Write the words.

Summary

Zoe's father is Canadian. Zoe's mother is Mexican. Zoe's

family _____ in Korea. Zoe's friend is Mina.

X	A	P	X	X	E	I	M	G	H	U	Q	E	M	T
D	R	X	Q	O	W	X	G	L	S	V	G	I	L	Y
I	R	Z	Y	F	M	Y	R	E	C	V	H	N	Z	K
V	A	S	P	X	G	D	J	U	Z	R	B	M	T	O
I	Z	O	T	K	Y	J	E	V	Y	Q	N	E	T	R
Z	D	Q	B	W	F	B	J	D	Z	M	Z	X	S	E
D	T	C	E	J	H	A	M	W	U	U	E	I	R	A
F	M	V	G	Z	S	C	S	K	E	J	G	C	Q	N
P	F	X	B	F	L	M	J	O	H	W	W	O	Z	C
V	B	H	T	L	J	A	L	C	W	K	B	S	G	A
X	A	B	Q	O	U	J	W	A	V	J	O	L	P	N
O	H	W	T	U	V	X	R	H	Z	P	N	O	T	A
H	S	O	Q	C	V	Z	I	U	O	A	G	Y	F	D
X	P	Q	L	P	C	D	G	E	C	I	Z	Z	R	A
R	T	B	I	S	L	A	N	D	I	H	V	G	Q	Z

 Write the words. Then find them in the puzzle.

1 _____

2 _____

3 _____

4 _____

UNIT 3

Kari's Neighbor

 Teacher's Book p.140

Who are your neighbors?

Mr. Conti is Kari's neighbor. He lives next door. So his house is next to Kari's house. Kari likes Mr. Conti. He is very kind. Is Kari hungry? Mr. Conti gives Kari food. And he is funny. He tells great jokes. He tells a story. Then Kari laughs.

New Words

neighbor

kind

funny

laugh

Part A. Spell the Words

1.

nei__bor

(A) ch

(B) gh

(C) sh

2.

la_gh

(A) u

(B) o

(C) a

Part B. Situational Writing

3.

Mr. Conti is _____.

(A) bad

(B) kind

(C) mean

4.

Mr. Conti reads a _____ story.

(A) sad

(B) long

(C) funny

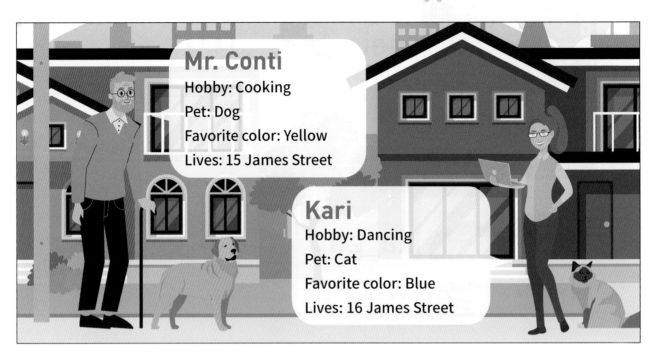

5. Where does Mr. Conti live?

   (A) 14 James Street
   (B) 15 James Street
   (C) 16 James Street

6. What is true about Kari?

   (A) She has a dog.
   (B) She likes dancing.
   (C) She loves yellow best.

Part D. General Reading and Retelling

> Mr. Conti is Kari's neighbor. He lives next door. So his house is next to Kari's house. Kari likes Mr. Conti. He is very kind. Is Kari hungry? Mr. Conti gives Kari food. And he is funny. He tells great jokes. He tells a story. Then Kari laughs.

7. What is the best title?

   (A) Kari Gets a Pet
   (B) Welcome to Kari's House
   (C) Kari's Next Door Neighbor

8. Where does Mr. Conti live?

   (A) next to Kari's house
   (B) behind Kari's house
   (C) in front of Kari's house

9. What is Mr. Conti like?

   (A) He is shy.
   (B) He is scary.
   (C) He is funny.

10. What does Kari do?

   (A) cook for Mr. Conti
   (B) tell Mr. Conti jokes
   (C) laugh at Mr. Conti's stories

Listening Practice

 Listen and write.

  MP3 PS3-3

Kari's Neighbor

Mr. Conti is Kari's ¹_____. He lives next door. So his house is next to Kari's house. Kari likes Mr. Conti. He is very ²_____. Is Kari hungry? Mr. Conti gives Kari food. And he is ³_____. He tells great jokes. He tells a story. Then Kari ⁴_____.

Word Bank

kind   laughs

kaynd   lafs

neighbor   punny

naybor   funny

 Listen. Pause. Say each sentence.

  MP3 PS3-3G

Writing Practice

 Write the words.

1

n				b	

2

k		

3

f			

4

l			

 Write the words.

Summary

Mr. Conti is Kari's next door _____. Mr. Conti is very kind and funny.

Word Puzzle

J	S	I	T	S	Y	T	E	T	N	R	I	B	G	V
V	L	L	V	F	I	N	X	J	U	V	N	B	L	Q
L	S	M	O	R	I	Y	Q	F	I	P	D	K	K	N
B	U	Z	X	Q	F	Z	N	Y	W	O	L	H	K	M
K	E	C	R	H	D	S	G	W	K	U	G	U	B	I
W	N	C	V	H	O	O	Z	W	M	B	T	B	N	S
J	C	E	X	W	Z	T	N	U	Q	M	U	X	N	W
Y	U	N	L	I	J	X	E	W	S	U	P	B	L	N
Y	P	F	O	E	I	T	I	M	U	L	F	G	H	D
H	A	J	H	P	I	T	G	F	Q	O	B	Z	L	J
E	Q	Y	H	M	K	D	H	C	S	T	P	E	Y	T
N	J	P	Z	N	K	P	B	S	H	L	F	L	S	T
R	N	N	Q	Q	I	G	O	B	F	U	N	N	Y	P
D	K	K	K	L	N	D	R	O	U	Q	A	P	G	X
A	H	W	K	M	D	J	C	H	Z	L	A	U	G	H

🔍 Write the words. Then find them in the puzzle.

1 _____ 2 _____ 3 _____ 4 _____

Teacher's Book p.143

UNIT 4

Anna and Hennie

What color is your hair?
What color are your eyes?

Anna and Hennie are nine years old. They are best friends. Anna has one younger brother. Hennie has two older sisters. Anna and Hennie have curly hair. But Anna's hair is long. And Hennie's hair is short. Anna's hair is brown. Hennie's hair is black. On Saturday they wear nice clothes. They are in the school concert!

New Words

curly

old

young

brown

Part A. Spell the Words

1.

c_rly

(A)　a

(B)　e

(C)　u

2.

con_ert

(A)　c

(B)　s

(C)　k

Part B. Situational Writing

3.

Hennie has two _____.

(A)　dogs

(B)　sisters

(C)　brothers

4.

Anna has _____ hair.

(A)　red

(B)　brown

(C)　purple

5. What is true about Jimmy?

(A) He is short.

(B) He has straight hair.

(C) He wears a purple shirt.

6. What is NOT true about Charlie?

(A) He is tall.

(B) He is slim.

(C) He has black hair.

Part D. General Reading and Retelling

> Anna and Hennie are nine years old. They are best friends. Anna has one younger brother. Hennie has two older sisters. Anna and Hennie have curly hair. But Anna's hair is long. And Hennie's hair is short. Anna's hair is brown. Hennie's hair is black. On Saturday they wear nice clothes. They are in the school concert!

7. What is the best title?

    (A) A Large Family
    (B) Three Brothers
    (C) Two Best Friends

8. What is true about Anna?

    (A) She has curly hair.
    (B) She is ten years old.
    (C) She has a younger sister.

9. What is NOT true about Hennie?

    (A) She has long hair.
    (B) She is nine years old.
    (C) She has two older sisters.

10. What happens on Saturday?

    (A) a school trip
    (B) a school concert
    (C) a school picture day

Listening Practice

 Listen and write.

  MP3 PS3-4

Anna and Hennie

Anna and Hennie are nine years old. They are best friends.

Anna has one ¹ [_____] brother. Hennie has two

² [_____] sisters. Anna and Hennie have ³ [_____]

hair. But Anna's hair is long. And Hennie's hair is short.

Anna's hair is ⁴ [_____]. Hennie's hair is black. On

Saturday they wear nice clothes. They are in the school

concert!

Word Bank

blown	order
curly	younger
brown	yunger
older	colly

 Listen. Pause. Say each sentence.

  MP3 PS3-4G

Writing Practice

 Write the words.

1

c			

2

3

y			

4

b			

 Write the words.

Summary

Anna and Hennie are best _____. They are nine years old. They have curly hair. They are in a concert.

A	K	B	O	E	D	X	R	K	V	C	G	D	W	Q
O	J	V	C	U	I	K	T	X	F	G	K	M	V	J
O	Z	G	U	O	U	H	N	U	Q	O	O	T	V	R
S	R	S	R	O	H	T	U	A	O	L	P	W	Y	D
Y	J	G	L	J	H	Z	N	D	M	D	R	S	X	O
Z	M	W	Y	H	R	K	M	C	L	I	Y	H	Y	I
Q	P	G	F	R	M	X	B	F	L	J	N	I	O	J
B	X	B	Z	P	H	C	L	H	R	D	H	E	U	T
R	N	X	R	M	H	B	B	M	H	C	G	B	N	N
Y	C	H	H	P	F	B	W	L	E	K	Z	V	G	N
X	K	J	Z	H	Z	R	P	L	I	C	H	P	I	V
P	A	S	V	U	V	O	V	O	C	Z	D	R	N	J
P	R	P	I	Y	E	W	X	U	Z	A	A	V	B	S
R	H	Z	K	L	P	N	O	E	D	I	E	Z	C	B
H	X	L	G	V	G	X	O	M	S	Y	D	U	P	I

Write the words. Then find them in the puzzle.

1 _____

2 _____

3 _____

4 _____

CHAPTER REVIEW

 Match the pictures to the correct words.

 Teacher's Book p.146

brown

Canada

curly

drive

funny

island

kind

Korea

laugh

loud

Mexico

neighbor

old

sometimes

steal

young

CHAPTER 2

Nature

UNIT 5

Paul and the Weather

Teacher's Book
p.147

What is the weather like today?

Paul likes sunny days. He likes bright days. But on Monday it rains. There are dark clouds in the sky. Paul can't go out. He hates rainy days. He sits at home. He waits for the sun. Then the rain stops! What is outside? Paul sees a rainbow. He sees many colors. Now he likes rainy days too.

New Words

sun

rainbow

bright

color

Part A. Spell the Words

1.

cl__d

(A)　oi

(B)　au

(C)　ou

2.

_un

(A)　f

(B)　g

(C)　s

Part B. Situational Writing

3.

Rainbow has many _____.

(A)　colors

(B)　clouds

(C)　names

4.

It _____ on Monday.

(A)　rains

(B)　snows

(C)　thunders

5. What is in the sky?

    (A) sun
    (B) clouds
    (C) rainbow

6. What is the weather like?

    (A) rainy
    (B) bright
    (C) snowy

Part D. General Reading and Retelling

Paul likes sunny days. He likes bright days. But on Monday it rains. There are dark clouds in the sky. Paul can't go out. He hates rainy days. He sits at home. He waits for the sun. Then the rain stops! What is outside? Paul sees a rainbow. He sees many colors. Now he likes rainy days too.

7. What is the best title?

   (A) Paul Goes Out
   (B) Paul and His Books
   (C) Paul and the Weather

8. How is the weather on Monday?

   (A) rainy
   (B) sunny
   (C) snowy

9. Where is Paul?

   (A) at home
   (B) at school
   (C) at the park

10. What does Paul see after the rain?

   (A) the sun
   (B) a rainbow
   (C) some stars

Listening Practice

 Listen and write.

  MP3 PS3-5

Paul and the Weather

Paul likes sunny days. He likes ¹_____ days. But on Monday it rains. There are dark clouds in the sky. Paul can't go out. He hates rainy days. He sits at home. He waits for the ²_____. Then the rain stops! What is outside? Paul sees a ³_____. He sees many ⁴_____. Now he likes rainy days too.

Word Bank

sun	colors
rainbow	callers
son	brit
lainbow	bright

 Listen. Pause. Say each sentence.

 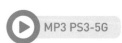 MP3 PS3-5G

Writing Practice

 Write the words.

1 | | | |

2 | r | | | | o | |

3 | b | | | | |

4 | | | | r |

 Write the words.

Summary

Paul likes sunny days. He hates rainy days. But then he sees a

_____. Now he likes rainy days, too.

Word Puzzle

Q	J	W	N	J	N	F	S	P	X	N	S	Q	S	O
T	B	X	X	N	Z	L	X	M	P	K	X	Y	G	B
A	Y	I	A	H	Y	B	B	X	I	S	U	N	O	R
Q	N	U	C	C	Q	H	C	M	D	M	X	F	D	I
K	Q	H	O	K	Q	M	D	D	X	V	L	R	X	G
Y	R	E	L	P	A	J	D	E	U	D	U	J	M	H
N	K	S	O	C	B	N	X	N	S	C	L	V	P	T
S	V	O	R	A	I	N	B	O	W	I	G	Y	H	Z
N	H	V	H	V	A	J	Q	J	B	B	I	F	S	Q
R	J	Z	U	V	O	S	Q	V	U	H	P	B	J	Q
J	Q	G	E	F	S	J	W	F	D	E	K	B	S	I
Z	K	H	X	H	B	F	D	B	E	H	C	C	T	Z
L	N	F	X	Y	E	A	W	X	F	S	G	B	G	Y
R	X	K	W	Q	U	S	E	F	W	Y	B	F	F	L
F	V	A	M	Y	V	T	K	F	K	M	Q	J	K	S

  Write the words. Then find them in the puzzle.

1 _____

2 _____

3 _____

4 _____

UNIT 6

What Bug Is It?

Teacher's Book p.150

Do you like bugs?
Look at the picture. Name three bugs.

It is an insect. It is smaller than a spider. It can live one year. It is red with black spots. Its eggs are yellow or white. It has wings. So it can fly. It lives in grass. It also lives on leaves. It eats bad bugs. So people like it. It is not a butterfly. What is it?

New Words

egg

spider

butterfly

wing

Part A. Spell the Words

1.

sp_der

(A)   i

(B)   o

(C)   y

2.

bu__erfly

(A)   th

(B)   dd

(C)   tt

Part B. Situational Writing

3.

It has black _____.

(A)   tails

(B)   spots

(C)   wings

4.

There are many _____.

(A)   bugs

(B)   leaves

(C)   flowers

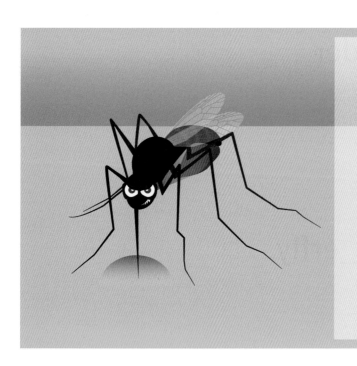

Mosquito!

Q How long do mosquitoes live?
A Some live only 10 days.
Some live 56 days.

Q Do all mosquitoes bite?
A No.

Q What do mosquitoes like?
A They like type O blood.

Q Does Earth need mosquitoes?
A Yes. Many animals eat them.
Mosquitoes can be good.

5. How long can some mosquitoes live?

(A) 56 days
(B) 100 days
(C) 156 days

6. What is NOT true about mosquitoes?

(A) They all bite.
(B) They like blood.
(C) They can be good.

Part D. General Reading and Retelling

It is an insect. It is smaller than a spider. It can live one year. It is red with black spots. Its eggs are yellow or white. It has wings. So it can fly. It lives in grass. It also lives on leaves. It eats bad bugs. So people like it. It is not a butterfly. What is it?

7. What is it?

   (A) a spider
   (B) a ladybug
   (C) a mosquito

8. Where does it live?

   (A) in grass
   (B) in the ocean
   (C) in swimming pools

9. Why do people like it?

   (A) It cannot fly.
   (B) It is very big.
   (C) It eats bad bugs.

10. What color are its eggs?

   (A) red
   (B) blue
   (C) yellow

Listening Practice

 Listen and write.

 MP3 PS3-6

What Bug Is It?

It is an insect. It is smaller than a ¹ _____. It can live one year. It is red with black spots. Its ² _____ are yellow or white. It has ³ _____. So it can fly. It lives in grass. It also lives on leaves. It eats bad bugs. So people like it. It is not a ⁴ _____. What is it?

Word Bank

spyder	eggs
egs	wigns
wings	butterfly
buterfly	spider

 Listen. Pause. Say each sentence.

 MP3 PS3-6G

Writing Practice

 Write the words.

1

2
	p			

3
b						l	

4
		n	

 Write the words.

Summary

A(An) _____ is smaller than a spider. It is red with black spots. It has wings.

Word Puzzle

E	F	I	P	F	B	H	C	L	I	T	O	T	B	A
U	N	L	E	U	Q	R	Q	U	O	Y	L	Q	L	M
Q	L	L	I	M	B	K	G	N	F	E	D	C	Y	D
V	C	L	O	S	E	R	K	Q	E	F	I	Y	E	H
M	K	W	Z	O	N	K	Q	Q	G	K	E	G	S	T
Q	N	J	N	A	N	M	A	W	G	E	E	K	S	Y
K	L	B	E	Y	W	X	V	F	W	J	T	E	J	B
U	B	G	M	O	N	L	P	S	N	T	H	W	U	U
Q	E	Z	V	X	R	U	V	J	G	V	T	A	O	T
E	M	D	W	X	W	I	Z	B	L	X	G	A	X	T
S	F	E	I	Z	Y	L	A	J	B	K	W	O	A	E
U	R	S	N	Y	E	J	F	Z	V	R	T	Z	C	R
N	Y	J	G	E	P	A	O	O	F	B	J	W	V	F
M	S	O	J	P	R	A	Z	W	E	X	A	X	P	L
H	C	S	P	I	D	E	R	O	L	S	Z	F	A	Y

Write the words. Then find them in the puzzle.

1 _____

2 _____

3 _____

4 _____

UNIT 7

A Family Trip

Teacher's Book p.153

Do you like beaches?
Is there a beach near you?

Where is Maria's family? They are on Jeju Island. Where do Maria's grandparents go? They go up Halla Mountain. It is very high. Where do Maria's parents go? They go to Bijarim Forest. The trees are 800 years old. What does Maria's brother do? He swims in the sea. The sea is clear. What does Maria do? She makes a sand castle at the beach.

New Words

mountain

forest

sea

beach

Part A. Spell the Words

1.

_ountain

(A) l

(B) m

(C) n

2.

S___

(A) ae

(B) ea

(C) ia

Part B. Situational Writing

3.

This is my favorite _____ on the island!

(A) zoo

(B) river

(C) beach

4.

There are _____ in Bijarim Forest.

(A) fish

(B) trees

(C) birds

5. What is this place?

(A) a jungle
(B) a rainforest
(C) the countryside

6. What is NOT in the picture?

(A) a pig
(B) a cow
(C) a farm

Part D. General Reading and Retelling

> Where is Maria's family? They are on Jeju Island. Where do Maria's grandparents go? They go up Halla Mountain. It is very high. Where do Maria's parents go? They go to Bijarim Forest. The trees are 800 years old. What does Maria's brother do? He swims in the sea. The sea is clear. What does Maria do? She makes a sand castle at the beach.

7. What is the best title?

   (A) Maria's Sad Day
   (B) Maria's Family Trip
   (C) Maria's Grandparents

8. Where does Maria's family NOT go?

   (A) to a sea
   (B) to a river
   (C) to a forest

9. What does Maria's brother do?

   (A) make a castle
   (B) swim in the sea
   (C) climb a mountain

10. Where are the trees 800 years old?

   (A) in the sea
   (B) at Bijarim Forest
   (C) on Halla Mountain

Listening Practice

 Listen and write.

  MP3 PS3-7

A Family Trip

Where is Maria's family? They are on Jeju Island. Where do Maria's grandparents go? They go up Halla ¹_____. It is very high. Where do Maria's parents go? They go to Bijarim ²_____. The trees are 800 years old. What does Maria's brother do? He swims in the ³_____ . The sea is clear. What does Maria do? She makes a sand castle at the ⁴_____.

Word Bank

Porest	beash
Mountain	see
Montan	Forest
beach	sea

 Listen. Pause. Say each sentence.

  MP3 PS3-7G

✏️ Writing Practice

 Write the words.

1

m					n

2

	o			

3

4

b			

 Write the words.

Summary

Maria's family _____ to Jeju Island. They go to

a mountain and a forest. Maria makes a sand castle.

Word Puzzle

J	G	K	C	L	Q	M	T	R	S	W	J	G	Q	R
T	U	M	I	N	X	N	Z	V	G	Q	U	Q	C	U
D	Q	O	X	P	T	O	X	Z	C	Y	G	M	E	V
O	D	U	P	H	M	K	S	V	L	U	O	M	Q	N
R	T	N	Q	S	Z	G	O	K	Q	X	M	W	J	H
P	F	T	P	A	B	C	U	I	I	V	K	N	S	H
G	F	A	I	H	L	O	V	H	L	W	Q	H	A	Y
I	Q	I	N	R	J	R	V	F	X	O	M	K	E	B
R	F	N	A	S	V	D	T	O	X	E	V	J	G	B
E	E	B	E	O	J	Z	C	R	W	B	E	A	C	H
W	K	T	I	P	O	Y	P	E	J	B	Q	Y	E	L
M	S	E	A	R	G	M	N	S	M	X	W	T	S	D
W	E	U	L	U	C	G	B	T	B	A	F	D	X	L
M	Q	G	Z	U	V	W	G	R	P	G	G	F	C	E
N	Y	T	E	A	U	W	M	F	W	U	V	U	Y	H

🔍 Write the words. Then find them in the puzzle.

1 _____   2 _____   3 _____   4 _____

UNIT 8

Teacher's Book p.157

Giraffes

Where do giraffes live?
What do giraffes eat?

Giraffes have very long necks. They have short ears. They have no front teeth on top. They eat leaves in tall trees. They have brown spots. Do they sleep a long time? No, they do not! Giraffes only sleep thirty minutes a day. They stand up and sleep. They are strong. They can kick and kill lions. June 21st is World Giraffe Day.

New Words

giraffe

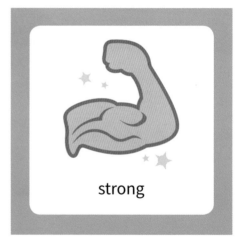

strong

kick

teeth

Part A. Spell the Words

1.

giraff_

(A) e

(B) u

(C) i

2.

_ick

(A) c

(B) k

(C) h

Part B. Situational Writing

3.

Giraffes eat _____ in tall trees.

(A) bugs

(B) fruits

(C) leaves

4.

Giraffes are strong and can win _____.

(A) lions

(B) tigers

(C) rabbits

UNIT 8 Giraffes

5. What are the people doing?

    (A) They are on a safari.
    (B) They are looking at the stars.
    (C) They are reading animal books.

6. What animals can they see?

    (A) deer
    (B) penguins
    (C) kangaroos

Part D. General Reading and Retelling

Giraffes have very long necks. They have short ears. They have no front teeth on top. They eat leaves in tall trees. They have brown spots. Do they sleep a long time? No, they do not! Giraffes only sleep thirty minutes a day. They stand up and sleep. They are strong. They can kick and kill lions. June 21st is World Giraffe Day.

7. What is very long?

(A) giraffe's ears
(B) giraffe's necks
(C) giraffe's front teeth

8. When is World Giraffe Day?

(A) in April
(B) in June
(C) in July

9. What is true about giraffes?

(A) They can kill lions.
(B) They eat fruits in trees.
(C) They sleep a long time.

10. Where is this passage, probably?

(A) at a zoo
(B) in a restaurant
(C) near a swimming pool

Listening Practice

 Listen and write.

 MP3 PS3-8

Giraffes

[1] _____ have very long necks. They have short ears. They have no front [2] _____ on top. They eat leaves in tall trees. They have brown spots. Do they sleep a long time? No, they do not! Giraffes only sleep thirty minutes a day. They stand up and sleep. They are [3] _____. They can [4] _____ and kill lions. June 21st is World Giraffe Day.

Word Bank

strong	teeth
strog	Jiraffes
kik	Giraffes
kick	tith

 Listen. Pause. Say each sentence.

 MP3 PS3-8G

Writing Practice

 Write the words.

1

| | i | | | f | |

2

| s | | | | |

3

| k | | | |

4

| t | | | |

 Write the words.

Summary

_____ have very long necks, short ears, and brown spots. They eat leaves. They are strong.

Word Puzzle

E	B	D	J	P	G	F	U	I	G	M	K	I	R	K
W	V	Q	E	T	O	Q	A	P	I	E	O	S	B	B
Z	L	J	J	P	M	U	S	T	R	O	N	G	K	J
I	V	U	N	Z	Q	D	P	J	A	A	A	P	X	P
M	U	U	X	S	Q	N	W	P	F	O	N	Z	O	L
S	W	S	T	E	E	T	H	P	F	Y	N	K	W	K
O	E	S	D	F	B	I	O	W	E	O	B	E	A	P
S	H	K	I	C	K	X	W	D	J	Z	Z	F	P	E
S	Q	X	B	S	Q	M	W	O	Q	D	U	N	G	Y
B	N	G	N	O	H	J	V	F	R	D	K	K	N	G
B	S	X	A	R	Q	F	Z	P	Z	B	Z	E	V	J
T	K	Y	I	G	W	A	U	V	E	E	K	G	Y	S
R	E	N	H	A	I	V	D	M	S	O	K	N	V	B
I	U	Y	O	F	P	T	I	F	Y	A	Y	U	S	W
I	T	Q	V	M	M	H	D	O	Z	I	E	H	O	X

 Write the words. Then find them in the puzzle.

1 _____ 2 _____ 3 _____ 4 _____

CHAPTER REVIEW

 Match the pictures to the correct words.

 Teacher's Book p.160

beach

bright

butterfly

color

egg

forest

giraffe

kick

mountain

rainbow

sea

spider

strong

sun

teeth

wing

CHAPTER 3

Places

UNIT 9

Martin Gets Cookies

Teacher's Book p.161

You go to a bakery. What do you buy?

Martin likes sweet things. Today he wants cookies. But Martin has no money. So he goes to the bank. He gets money. He passes by his school. He passes a restaurant. He finds a bakery. He buys five cookies. He buys some milk. He feels happy. He runs home. He eats the cookies there. He smiles.

New Words

bank

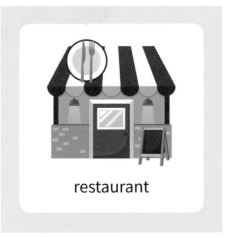

restaurant

bakery

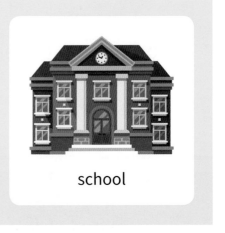

school

1.

rest__rant

(A) au

(B) eu

(C) ua

2.

bake_y

(A) l

(B) r

(C) w

Part B. Situational Writing

3.

Martin likes _____.

(A) cakes

(B) bread

(C) cookies

4.

I want to have a cup of _____.

(A) milk

(B) home

(C) money

UNIT 9 Martin Gets Cookies

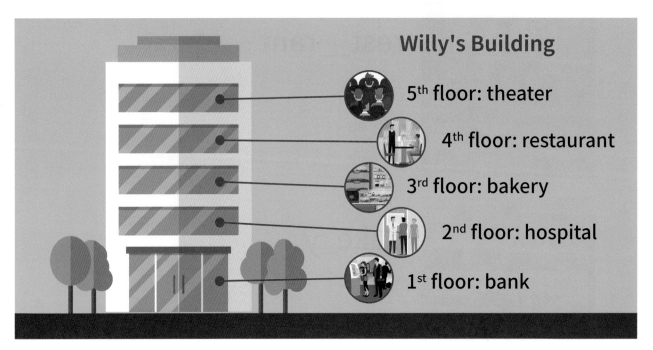

5.   Where is bakery?

   (A) 1st floor
   (B) 2nd floor
   (C) 3rd floor

6.   What is on the 4th floor?

   (A) park
   (B) theater
   (C) restaurant

Part D. General Reading and Retelling

Martin likes sweet things. Today he wants cookies. But Martin has no money. So he goes to the bank. He gets money. He passes by his school. He passes a restaurant. He finds a bakery. He buys five cookies. He buys some milk. He feels happy. He runs home. He eats the cookies there. He smiles.

7. What is the best title?

   (A) Martin Goes Home
   (B) Martin Gets Cookies
   (C) Martin Passes the Bank

8. What does Martin have today?

   (A) milk
   (B) juice
   (C) bread

9. What does Martin NOT see?

   (A) a bank
   (B) a post office
   (C) a restaurant

10. Where does Martin go today?

   (A) to school
   (B) to a bakery
   (C) to a restaurant

Listening Practice

 Listen and write.

  MP3 PS3-9

Martin Gets Cookies

Martin likes sweet things. Today he wants cookies. But Martin has no money. So he goes to the ¹ _____ . He gets money. He passes by his ² _____ . He passes a ³ _____ . He finds a ⁴ _____ . He buys five cookies. He buys some milk. He feels happy. He runs home. He eats the cookies there. He smiles.

Word Bank

school	restaurant
restarant	benk
scool	bank
bakery	bekery

 Listen. Pause. Say each sentence.

  MP3 PS3-9G

Writing Practice

 Write the words.

1 b

2 r r

3 b

4 s

 Write the words.

Summary

Martin wants cookies. He finds a _____. He

buys five cookies and some milk.

Word Puzzle

W	B	A	K	E	R	Y	A	E	B	O	M	U	E	Z
D	J	H	R	W	T	J	Z	L	R	X	N	Z	O	J
J	C	Z	N	B	S	X	B	E	E	G	I	G	N	W
H	W	F	H	C	V	R	Z	D	S	C	H	O	O	L
G	F	L	Q	X	G	R	L	N	T	Y	P	D	O	V
E	Q	O	O	J	G	Y	J	W	A	S	Z	F	V	Y
I	O	H	H	F	N	D	N	A	U	X	D	M	S	D
J	J	R	J	F	S	Q	I	S	R	D	W	U	H	S
W	R	S	A	V	C	M	Y	T	A	O	Z	C	X	F
M	A	L	M	V	P	H	M	I	N	E	F	C	C	J
M	S	G	M	E	I	W	L	I	T	R	S	V	R	B
L	V	A	J	F	V	X	N	I	C	A	B	A	N	K
R	O	Q	O	T	J	V	S	I	A	W	A	Q	W	D
C	W	Z	G	D	D	B	X	V	L	A	Y	L	Q	U
O	Z	K	H	S	V	S	X	J	I	H	A	C	B	D

 Write the words. Then find them in the puzzle.

1 _____ 2 _____ 3 _____ 4 _____

Teacher's Book
p.164

UNIT 10

Kate Loves Her Teddy Bear

What is your favorite toy?

Kate's favorite toy is a teddy bear. She puts it on her bed. And she sleeps with it. But the teddy bear is too old. It becomes dirty. So her father buys her a new toy. It's a robot. It can walk, sing, and dance. The teddy bear can do nothing. It just lies on her bed. But Kate still loves her teddy bear. It is her best friend.

New Words

teddy bear

toy

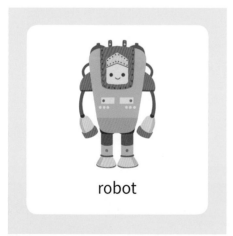

robot

friend

1.

wal_

(A)   c

(B)   k

(C)   q

2.

b__r

(A)   oi

(B)   ea

(C)   oa

Part B. Situational Writing

3.

Kate's favorite toy is _____.

(A)   old

(B)   clean

(C)   orange

4.

The robot can sing and _____.

(A)   eat

(B)   write

(C)   dance

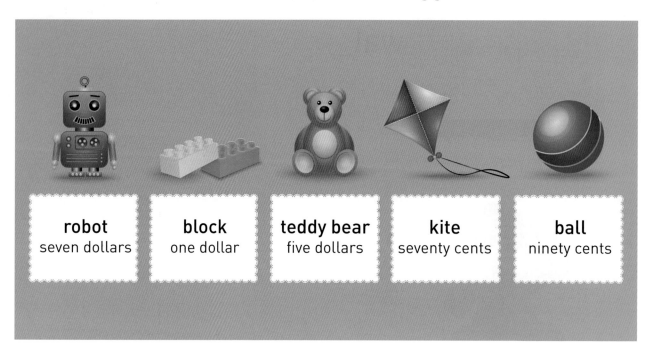

robot	block	teddy bear	kite	ball
seven dollars	one dollar	five dollars	seventy cents	ninety cents

5. How much are three blocks?

    (A) one dollar

    (B) three dollars

    (C) five dollars

6. What can you buy in this toy shop?

    (A) a kite

    (B) a boat

    (C) a piggy bank

Part D. General Reading and Retelling

Kate's favorite toy is a teddy bear. She puts it on her bed. And she sleeps with it. But the teddy bear is too old. It becomes dirty. So her father buys her a new toy. It's a robot. It can walk, sing, and dance. The teddy bear can do nothing. It just lies on her bed. But Kate still loves her teddy bear. It is her best friend.

7. What is the best title?

   (A) Kate Buys a New Toy
   (B) Kate Can Do Many Things
   (C) Kate Loves Her Teddy Bear

8. What is Kate's favorite toy?

   (A) a kite
   (B) a robot
   (C) a teddy bear

9. What is true about Kate's teddy bear?

   (A) It is on her bed.
   (B) It is clean and new.
   (C) It can walk and sing.

10. What can the robot do?

   (A) write
   (B) paint
   (C) dance

 **Listening Practice**

 Listen and write.

  MP3 PS3-10

Kate Loves Her Teddy Bear

Kate's favorite ¹ _____ is a teddy bear. She puts it on her bed. And she sleeps with it. But the teddy ² _____ is too old. It becomes dirty. So her father buys her a new toy. It's a ³ _____. It can walk, sing, and dance. The teddy bear can do nothing. It just lies on her bed. But Kate still loves her teddy bear. It is her best ⁴ _____.

Word Bank

toi	toy
robot	lobot
bear	priend
friend	ber

 Listen. Pause. Say each sentence.

  MP3 PS3-10G

Writing Practice

 Write the words.

1
| t | | | | | | r |

2
| | | |

3
| | | b | | |

4
| | r | | | |

 Write the words.

Summary

Kate's favorite _____ is a teddy bear. Her father buys her a new robot. Kate still loves her teddy bear.

Word Puzzle

J	K	D	J	O	H	E	L	Y	L	I	N	Q	U	T
N	A	L	G	S	Y	U	Q	D	O	G	S	W	D	H
X	L	B	R	N	E	T	F	R	I	E	N	D	E	L
K	H	F	T	O	Y	S	V	A	D	W	M	P	Y	P
L	P	G	Y	T	I	P	P	G	Q	L	Y	B	I	W
S	U	T	E	D	D	Y	B	E	A	R	Z	W	H	Y
O	Y	E	C	F	S	H	N	J	I	S	Q	F	E	W
X	T	L	D	X	Q	R	V	Q	F	J	R	R	A	S
F	D	H	N	B	V	V	V	L	P	H	A	O	T	S
H	T	R	N	L	P	F	D	Y	U	Q	R	B	I	G
N	S	L	Z	Z	D	U	J	Z	O	E	J	O	I	J
P	M	H	Z	K	C	S	F	G	Z	X	C	T	I	A
D	U	K	U	X	J	O	W	H	X	M	M	K	P	C
Q	U	K	G	N	P	A	W	V	I	M	W	F	O	S
P	O	L	O	K	R	V	L	I	X	Q	X	R	F	I

 Write the words. Then find them in the puzzle.

1 _____ 2 _____ 3 _____ 4 _____

UNIT 11

 Teacher's Book p.167

Finding Things

Find the way to the treasure.
Which way is it?

My friends and I have a treasure hunt. I hide treasures in the forest. A robot is under the rock. A kite is in the tree. A pink doll is between some flowers and the lake. Some chocolate is in front of the hill. My friends find the things. They are excited. They start here. Three, two, one. Start!

New Words

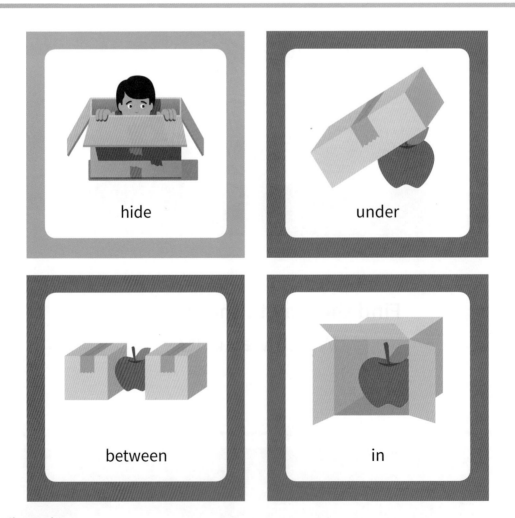

hide

under

between

in

Part A. Spell the Words

1.

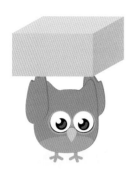

_nder

(A) u

(B) a

(C) e

2.

bet_een

(A) s

(B) w

(C) g

Part B. Situational Writing

3.

The kite is _____ the tree.

(A) on

(B) behind

(C) across from

4.

My friends are _____.

(A) sad

(B) sick

(C) excited

5. Where are they?

(A) street

(B) subway

(C) bus station

6. What is the thief doing?

(A) running away

(B) stealing the man's purse

(C) stealing the man's phone

Part D. General Reading and Retelling

My friends and I have a treasure hunt. I hide treasures in the forest. A robot is under the rock. A kite is in the tree. A pink doll is between some flowers and the lake. Some chocolate is in front of the hill. My friends find the things. They are excited. They start here. Three, two, one. Start!

7. What is the best title?

   (A) Run with Friends
   (B) Play a Game with Friends
   (C) Make a Robot with Friends

8. What do I do?

   (A) I find treasures.
   (B) I buy treasures.
   (C) I hide treasures.

9. Where is the robot?

   (A) in the tree
   (B) under the rock
   (C) between flowers and the lake

10. What is in front of the hill?

   (A) kite
   (B) doll
   (C) chocolate

UNIT 11 Finding Things

Listening Practice

 Listen and write.

  MP3 PS3-11

Finding Things

My friends and I have a treasure hunt. I ¹ _____ treasures in the forest. A robot is ² _____ the rock. A kite is ³ _____ the tree. A pink doll is ⁴ _____ some flowers and the lake. Some chocolate is in front of the hill. My friends find the things. They are excited. They start here. Three, two, one. Start!

Word Bank

in	under
between	inn
hide	betwin
undr	hid

 Listen. Pause. Say each sentence.

  MP3 PS3-11G

Writing Practice

 Write the words.

1

| h | | | |

2

| | | | r | |

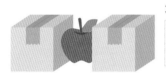

3

| b | | | w | | | |

4

| | |

 Write the words.

Summary

My friends and I have a treasure hunt. I _____ a

robot, a kite, a doll, and chocolate in the forest.

Word Puzzle

W	S	M	Z	K	G	L	I	F	H	R	H	M	X	W
E	B	E	T	W	E	E	N	X	N	K	E	K	J	S
K	D	Z	D	A	D	U	G	E	V	H	R	U	N	G
Y	Q	U	Q	D	D	M	U	F	S	A	C	K	A	W
V	M	Q	M	F	L	V	B	D	V	W	L	C	Y	Q
G	M	T	Q	R	A	D	D	I	L	F	O	H	K	U
C	H	B	O	O	U	T	K	H	I	D	E	O	H	S
D	G	W	K	A	Z	U	N	C	Q	W	A	N	I	C
J	W	U	Y	M	D	B	Z	B	C	D	Q	M	B	F
P	S	Q	K	C	L	X	N	G	V	F	M	G	B	T
I	X	E	Z	X	W	W	W	U	A	I	M	O	F	M
J	B	B	Z	Z	D	E	K	N	C	J	P	W	Z	D
J	G	Q	N	L	S	Z	G	D	W	M	B	Y	K	G
O	J	F	E	I	E	F	I	E	H	I	F	I	T	M
C	F	D	P	S	Y	P	D	R	V	P	S	P	P	Z

 Write the words. Then find them in the puzzle.

  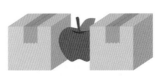 

1 _____   2 _____   3 _____   4 _____

UNIT 12

Finding a Place

 Teacher's Book p.170

Tim

Tim is going to the table. How?

We open a new restaurant. It is in our town. Its name is Spicy Tasty! It sells delicious hamburgers. Come to our restaurant! First, stand in front of the hospital. Then cross the road. And go straight. At the first corner, turn right. Spicy Tasty is on your left. It is between a cafe and a school.

New Words

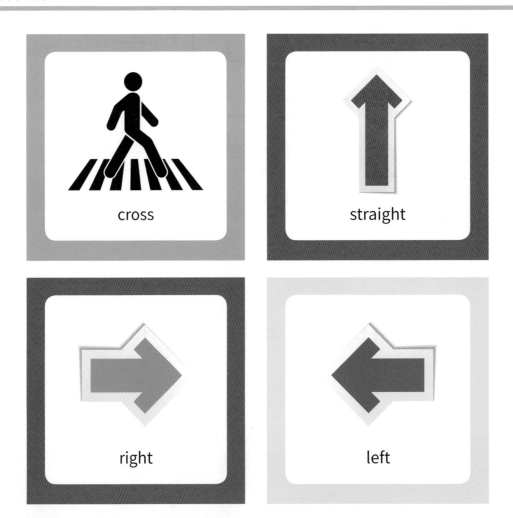

cross

straight

right

left

Part A. Spell the Words

1.

strai__t

(A) gh

(B) th

(C) zh

2.

righ_

(A) d

(B) t

(C) s

Part B. Situational Writing

3.

Spicy Tasty sells _____.

(A) coffee

(B) pizzas

(C) hamburgers

4.

I am in front of the _____.

(A) cafe

(B) hospital

(C) post office

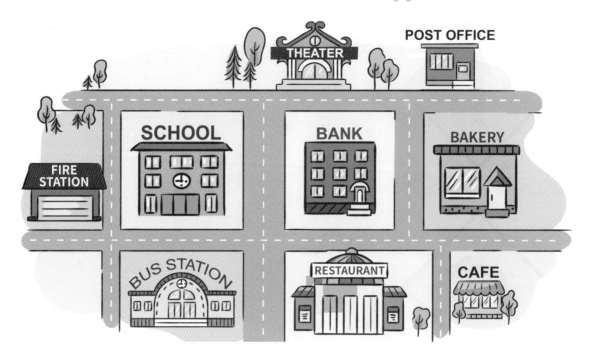

5. Where is the school?

    (A) next to the bakery

    (B) in front of the post office

    (C) across from the fire station

6. From the restaurant, how do you get to the theater?

    (A) Turn left.

    (B) Turn right.

    (C) Go straight.

Part D. General Reading and Retelling

We open a new restaurant. It is in our town. Its name is Spicy Tasty! It sells delicious hamburgers. Come to our restaurant! First, stand in front of the hospital. Then cross the road. And go straight. At the first corner, turn right. Spicy Tasty is on your left. It is between a cafe and a school.

7.   Where is Spicy Tasty?

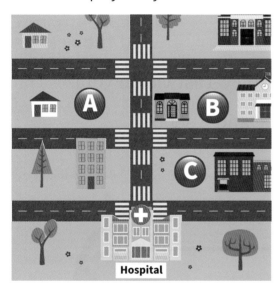

8.   What is Spicy Tasty?

(A) cafe
(B) school
(C) restaurant

9.   What is true about Spicy Tasty?

(A) It is 10 years old.
(B) It is next to school.
(C) It is inside the hospital.

10. What can you do with this passage?

(A) drive a car
(B) open a hospital
(C) find a restaurant

Listening Practice

 Listen and write.

  MP3 PS3-12

Finding a Place

We open a new restaurant. It is in our town. Its name is Spicy Tasty! It sells delicious hamburgers. Come to our restaurant! First, stand in front of the hospital. Then

¹ _____ the road. And go ² _____ . At the first corner, turn ³ _____ . Spicy Tasty is on your

⁴ _____ . It is between a cafe and a school.

Word Bank

cross	right
light	left
strait	straight
kross	reft

 Listen. Pause. Say each sentence.

 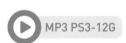 MP3 PS3-12G

Writing Practice

 Write the words.

1

		o		

2

s					t

3

	i		

4

		t	

UNIT 12   Finding a Place

 Write the words.

Summary

Here is the way to our _____. First, cross the road. Go straight. Turn right. It's on your left.

D	N	L	I	N	W	H	D	J	R	X	C	Z	P	V
C	D	B	Q	C	L	Z	V	X	K	D	T	C	B	F
H	R	U	O	I	E	I	G	T	L	Q	V	M	Z	H
Q	A	S	C	Q	F	S	D	T	R	M	H	I	X	H
K	H	V	R	J	T	N	U	I	H	I	Q	O	H	I
H	Q	L	O	H	C	T	J	L	Q	E	G	A	E	K
E	E	F	S	O	G	S	T	R	A	I	G	H	T	N
T	H	I	S	C	D	P	H	H	V	K	Y	S	L	G
Q	J	X	R	I	G	S	R	K	F	H	H	K	J	U
Y	W	B	W	J	W	Z	Y	U	I	P	F	Q	G	X
I	D	W	Z	Q	D	P	J	K	F	P	W	M	R	T
E	H	R	I	G	H	T	M	C	J	C	S	U	K	J
B	T	A	J	R	W	Y	A	H	W	P	E	D	M	N
F	J	B	I	U	Q	A	S	V	O	P	K	H	T	C
N	J	K	M	J	P	D	T	X	H	T	F	O	G	L

🔍 Write the words. Then find them in the puzzle.

1 _____   2 _____   3 _____   4 _____

CHAPTER REVIEW

 Match the pictures to the correct words.

Teacher's Book p.174

bakery

bank

block

cross

friend

hide

in

left

restaurant

right

robot

school

straight

teddy bear

toy

under

ANSWERS

UNIT 1 — PS3-1, p.11

	1	2	3	4	5	6	7	8	9	10
⏱	(A)	(A)	(A)	(A)	(C)	(B)	(A)	(C)	(A)	(A)
🎧	Sometimes	steal	drive	loud						
✏️	sometimes	steal	drive	loud	📄 police officer					
※	sometimes	steal	drive	loud						

UNIT 2 — PS3-2, p.19

	1	2	3	4	5	6	7	8	9	10
⏱	(A)	(A)	(C)	(B)	(B)	(B)	(A)	(A)	(C)	(A)
🎧	Canada	Mexico	Korea	islands						
✏️	Canada	Mexico	Korea	island	📄 lives					
※	Canada	Mexico	Korea	island						

UNIT 3 — PS3-3, p.27

	1	2	3	4	5	6	7	8	9	10
⏱	(B)	(A)	(B)	(C)	(B)	(B)	(C)	(A)	(C)	(C)
🎧	neighbor	kind	funny	laughs						
✏️	neighbor	kind	funny	laugh	📄 neighbor					
※	neighbor	kind	funny	laugh						

UNIT 4 — PS3-4, p.35

	1	2	3	4	5	6	7	8	9	10
⏱	(C)	(A)	(B)	(B)	(A)	(C)	(C)	(A)	(A)	(B)
🎧	younger	older	curly	brown						
✏️	curly	old	young	brown	📄 friends					
※	curly	old	young	brown						

UNIT 5 — PS3-5, p.45

	1	2	3	4	5	6	7	8	9	10
⏱	(C)	(C)	(A)	(A)	(B)	(A)	(C)	(A)	(A)	(B)
🎧	bright	sun	rainbow	colors						
✏️	sun	rainbow	bright	color	📄 rainbow					
※	sun	rainbow	bright	color						

UNIT 6 — PS3-6, p.53

	1	2	3	4	5	6	7	8	9	10
⏱	(A)	(C)	(B)	(A)	(A)	(A)	(B)	(A)	(C)	(C)
🎧	spider	eggs	wings	butterfly						
✏️	egg	spider	butterfly	wing	📄 ladybug					
※	egg	spider	butterfly	wing						

UNIT 7 — PS3-7, p.61

	1	2	3	4	5	6	7	8	9	10
⏱	(B)	(B)	(C)	(B)	(C)	(A)	(B)	(B)	(B)	(B)
🎧	Mountain	Forest	sea	beach						
✏️	mountain	forest	sea	beach	📄 travels					
※	mountain	forest	sea	beach						

UNIT 8 — PS3-8, p.69

	1	2	3	4	5	6	7	8	9	10
⏱	(A)	(B)	(C)	(A)	(A)	(A)	(B)	(B)	(A)	(A)
🎧	Giraffes	teeth	strong	kick						
✏️	giraffe	strong	kick	teeth	📄 Giraffes					
※	giraffe	strong	kick	teeth						

UNIT 9 — PS3-9, p.79

	1	2	3	4	5	6	7	8	9	10
⏱	(A)	(B)	(C)	(A)	(C)	(C)	(B)	(A)	(B)	(B)
🎧	bank	school	restaurant	bakery						
✏️	bank	restaurant	bakery	school	📄 bakery					
※	bank	restaurant	bakery	school						

UNIT 10 — PS3-10, p.87

	1	2	3	4	5	6	7	8	9	10
⏱	(B)	(B)	(A)	(C)	(B)	(A)	(C)	(C)	(A)	(C)
🎧	toy	bear	robot	friend						
✏️	teddy bear	toy	robot	friend	📄 toy					
※	teddy bear	toy	robot	friend						

UNIT 11 — PS3-11, p.95

	1	2	3	4	5	6	7	8	9	10
⏱	(A)	(B)	(A)	(C)	(B)	(B)	(B)	(C)	(B)	(C)
🎧	hide	under	in	between						
✏️	hide	under	between	in	📄 hide					
※	hide	under	between	in						

UNIT 12 — PS3-12, p.103

	1	2	3	4	5	6	7	8	9	10
⏱	(A)	(B)	(C)	(B)	(C)	(C)	(B)	(C)	(B)	(C)
🎧	cross	straight	right	left						
✏️	cross	straight	right	left	📄 restaurant					
※	cross	straight	right	left						